The Literary Life Commonplace Book

Second Edition

Stories will save the world.

The Literary Life Commonplace Book: Fairy
By Angelina Stanford, Cindy Rollins, and Thomas Banks
© 2020, 2021

Second Edition © 2021, First Edition © 2020
Cover Design © Blue Sky Daisies 2020, 2021
Book Design © Blue Sky Daisies 2020, 2021

Published by Blue Sky Daisies
blueskydaisies.net

ISBN 13:978-1-944435-19-6

The Literary Life Commonplace Book

Second Edition

This book belongs to:

_____.

If found, please contact me at this number:

_____.

The Literary Life Podcast Official Commonplace Book
Stories will save the world.

Visit us online at *www.theliterary.life.*

Subscribe to our podcast.

Join the conversation on our Facebook community:
The Literary Life Podcast Discussion Group

BLUE SKY DAISIES

What is a "commonplace book"?

From the Latin *locus communis*, the term "commonplace" refers to a common saying or proverb. Generally speaking, a "commonplace book" is a private collection of proverbs, quotations, and sketches—or anything that catches your interest—that one might keep in a notebook. Although you may wish to jot down your thoughts on various subjects, or sketch out a design you have in mind, literary commonplace books differ from diaries or journals in that they are specifically a place for keeping track of things you are reading or discovering.

From Angelina Stanford

The life of the mind can often feel unreal. I've felt envious of friends who have something tangible to show at the end of their work: paintings, sweaters, a blooming garden. But what do I have to show for the hours I spend with a book in hand? Nothing but thoughts. In 2015, at a time when I very much felt like a wanderer in my own life, I began a new reading journal. I had previously commonplaced rather sporadically. Fits and starts would best describe my efforts. But for the last five years, I have written down every book I have read and the date I completed it. And for the first time, I began to find genuine joy in the process of commonplacing. I luxuriated in the moment of slowing down, reflecting on what I read, contemplating why I wanted to remember this particular quote, and enjoying a sense of accomplishment every time I marked a book completed. Now, when I pick up my journal, I have something tangible to document how I spend my time, and I love thumbing through the pages and seeing a record of what I have read and what I thought about. My commonplace book is a passport bearing the stamps of where I have been in this literary life. I feel less like a wanderer and more like a pilgrim journeying to the holy places.

From Cindy Rollins

I am probably the least traditional when it comes to commonplacing, perhaps because my mother started new notebooks hourly, hiding them so no one would know she was recording her random thoughts and vitamin intake. These days my commonplacing habits include taking pictures of quotes with my phone, underlining things in my Kindle, keeping a file of quotes on Evernote, and adding written quotes to my actual commonplace book every day of the first week of January. Even so, it is jolly fun to keep the same notebook of quotes for many, many years. This January I will be using The Literary Life Podcast journals and I am looking forward to the the common life of sharing my pages and seeing yours too. To misquote an old friend, Kenneth Grahame, whom I have never met, "Believe me, my young friend, there is nothing—absolutely nothing—half so much worth doing as simply messing about in books." I have been messing about in books for a very long time now and commonplacing helps me remember the streams I have visited and the friends I have made whether they are real or not.

From Thomas Banks

"*Books think for me,*" wrote Charles Lamb, and I have come to feel the same way in my own reading life. I first began keeping commonplace books when I was in high school, at the behest of an English teacher. At first I did so half-heartedly, as I did half-heartedly most assigned work at that period of my life. Some years ago, while visiting my parents, I discovered the first such notebook that I kept in a corner of a bookshelf and read through its contents with a growing sense of embarrassment. Most of the entries were, as one might expect, statements and aphorisms of the kind that at the age of fifteen I would have thought profound, or boldly Promethean, or (and these the most comic) "philosophical." The sources from which I had drawn these morsels of wisdom ranged from Byron and Poe to Salinger, and from Sartre ("*Hell is other people.*") to Joe Strummer and Kurt Cobain ("*Oh well, whatever, nevermind.*"). Certain entries reminded me of futile intellectual disciplines I undertook at that age in the desire to appear deeper than I was; one entry from Kierkegaard reminded me of the time I tried to make sense of *Fear and Trembling,* and misunderstood it entirely. Twenty years later, I misunderstand it still.

Somehow the duty became a habit. I continue to keep notebooks full of passages from my reading, partially from a certain odd feeling of closeness to the minds of my favorite authors which I derive from writing out select verses, sentences and paragraphs that are the fruit of their imaginations. The practice is also useful to me in that it supplies a prop to my rather weak memory, through which so much of what I read passes like water through a sieve. So it is that books not only think for me, but remember for me as well.

Stories will save the world.

Index   *Record the main content of each page here for a handy reference.*

39.

40.

41.

42.

43.

44.

45.

46.

47.

48.

49.

50.

51.

52.

53.

54.

55.

56.

57.

58.

59.

60.

61.

62.

63.

64.

65.

66.

67.

68.

69.

70.

71.

72.

73.

74.

75.

76.

77.
78.
79.
80.
81.
82.
83.
84.
85.
86.
87.
88.
89.
90.
91.
92.
93.
94.
95.
96.
97.
98.
99.
100.
101.
102.
103.
104.
105.
106.
107.
108.
109.
110.
111.
112.
113.
114.

Index

20 for 2020 Challenge:	Title Chosen	Completed
A Shakespeare Play		
A Classic Detective Novel		
A Classic Children's Book		
A Contemporary Novel		
A Historical Fiction Novel		
An Ancient Greek Play		
A Collection of Short Stories		
A Biography or Memoir		
A Devotional Work		
A Book about Books		

20 for 2020 Challenge:	Title Chosen	Completed
A Foreign (Non-Western) Book		
A "Guilty Pleasure" Book		
An Intimidating Book You Have Avoided		
A Satire		
A Book of Essays		
A Book by a Minor Author		
A Classic Book by a Female Author		
A Complete Volume of Poetry by a Single Author		
An "Out of Your Comfort Zone" Book		
Reread a Book You Read in High School		

192021 Challenge:	Title Chosen	Completed

A Poetry Anthology
Anything from Mother Goose to "Q" (Oxford Book of English Verse by Sir Arthur Quiller-Couch)

A Book (or Selection) of Letters

A Book From Your To-Be-Read Stack

An Ancient Greek or Roman Work
A play, epic, or collection of myths

A Book on Education, Art, or Literature

A Victorian Novel

A Lesser-Known Book by a Well-Known Author

A Shakespeare Play

A Book You Have Avoided

192021 Challenge:	Title Chosen	Completed

Finish a Book You Started but Never Finished

A Literary Biography

Something Russian
A play, short story, novel, or novella

A Regional or Local Book
A book related in some way to your local area

A 14th, 15th, or 16th Century Book
a book written in, set in, or about

A Book in a Genre You Don't Normally Read

An Obscure Book Mentioned by Thomas Banks
Or any book mentioned on the podcast

A Light Comedic Novel
Like PG Wodehouse

An "Other World" Book

A Travel Book
(Anything from Travels with a Donkey to A Walk in the Woods)

⭐ 192021 Kids Challenge:	Title Chosen	Completed

A Book of Myths
Such as Tanglewood Tales by Nathaniel Hawthorne

Five Fairy Tales
Any selection you like

Five Poems by One Poet
Such as Robert Frost, Emily Dickinson, or any other poet

Read a Book Aloud to a Sibling or Friend

A History Biography
Such as Signature Biographies or Landmark or Childhood of Famous Americans or others

A Book Recommended by a Grandparent or Older Person

Ten Fables
Aesop is one author.

A Book by an Author You've Never Read Before

A 19th Century Children's Classic
Such as The Jungle Book or Little Women or many others

192021 Kids Challenge:	Title Chosen	Completed

A Middle Ages Book
Written in or set in the Middle Ages or Renaissance.
Men of Iron by Howard Pyle, for example.

A 20th Century Children's Classic
The Chronicles of Narnia were written in the 20th century
along with many others.

A Book You Have Avoided

Reread a Book

A Biography of a Composer, Artist, or Writer
You may like Opal Wheeler's artist biographies.

Five Tall Tales
American Tall Tales by Adrien Stoutenburg, for example

A Book Written or Set in Ancient Greece or Rome

A Mystery or Detective Novel
Anything from Encyclopedia Brown to Dorothy L. Sayers!

A Legend
Such as King Arthur or Robin Hood
Rosemary Sutcliffe writes many books in this genre.

A Shakespeare Play
Or a retelling of a Shakespeare play

2 for '22 Challenge:	Title Chosen	Completed
Poetry: Well Read Poem Podcast Poets		
Two poets from The Well Read Poem podcast.		
First Poet (11 poems)		
Second Poet (11 poems)		
Favorite Author of Your Favorite Author		
First Choice		
Second Choice		
Biography		
Someone Living		
Someone Dead		
Victorian Novel		
Man Author		
Woman Author		
Drama		
Comedy		
Tragedy		
Inklings		
By *an Inkling*		
About *an Inkling*		

2 for '22 Challenge:	Title Chosen	Completed
International		
Two books set in a country other than yours (fiction or non-fiction).		
First Choice		
Second Choice		
History/Biography/Topical		
Two books with "opposing" perspectives		
First Choice		
Second Choice		
Classic Literature		
New Read		
Re-Read		
Detective/Murder Mystery		
Golden Age Detective Novel		
Contemporary		
Essays		
11 essays from past decades or centuries		
11 essays from this century		

Reading Challenge: 2 for '22 for Kids
Go further up and further in.

2 for '22 Challenge:	Title Chosen	Completed
A Novel from the Golden Age of Children's Literature		
New Read		
Re-read		
A Book of Myths		
Greek/Roman		
Non-Greek/Roman		
A Shakespeare Play or Retelling		
A Comedy		
A Tragedy		
A Biography		
Of a Boy/Man		
Of a Girl/Woman		
Two Poets Featured on The Well Read Poem		
First Poet (11 poems)		
Second Poet (11 poems)		
Fairy Tales		
11 Grimm's Fairy Tales		
11 Non-Grimm's Fairy Tales		

2 for '22 Challenge:	Title Chosen	Completed
An Other World/Fantasy/Sci-Fi Book		
One by a Dead Author		
One by a Living Author		
Non-Fiction		
History		
Other than Histoy (Art, Science, Math, Nature, etc.)		
A Detective/Mystery Story		
One with a Boy Detective		
One with a Girl Detective		
A Favorite Author of Your Favorite Author		
First Choice		
Second Choice		
International		
Two books set in a country other than yours (fiction or non-fiction).		
First Choice		
Second Choice		

Fiction

Title	Author	Recommended by

Non-Fiction

Title	Author	Recommended by

Read-Alouds

Title	*Author*	*Recommended by*

Poetry

Title	*Author*	*Recommended by*

Fairy Tales

Title	Author	Recommended by

Classic Works

Title	Author	Recommended by

Devotional

Title	Author	Recommended by

Bestsellers

Title	Author	Recommended by

Reading Log

Title	Author	Date Read	Rating
			☆☆☆☆☆
			☆☆☆☆☆
			☆☆☆☆☆
			☆☆☆☆☆
			☆☆☆☆☆
			☆☆☆☆☆
			☆☆☆☆☆
			☆☆☆☆☆
			☆☆☆☆☆
			☆☆☆☆☆
			☆☆☆☆☆
			☆☆☆☆☆
			☆☆☆☆☆
			☆☆☆☆☆
			☆☆☆☆☆
			☆☆☆☆☆
			☆☆☆☆☆
			☆☆☆☆☆
			☆☆☆☆☆
			☆☆☆☆☆

Reading Log

Title	Author	Date Read	Rating
			☆☆☆☆☆
			☆☆☆☆☆
			☆☆☆☆☆
			☆☆☆☆☆
			☆☆☆☆☆
			☆☆☆☆☆
			☆☆☆☆☆
			☆☆☆☆☆
			☆☆☆☆☆
			☆☆☆☆☆
			☆☆☆☆☆
			☆☆☆☆☆
			☆☆☆☆☆
			☆☆☆☆☆
			☆☆☆☆☆
			☆☆☆☆☆
			☆☆☆☆☆
			☆☆☆☆☆
			☆☆☆☆☆
			☆☆☆☆☆

Reading Log

Title	Author	Date Read	Rating
			☆☆☆☆☆
			☆☆☆☆☆
			☆☆☆☆☆
			☆☆☆☆☆
			☆☆☆☆☆
			☆☆☆☆☆
			☆☆☆☆☆
			☆☆☆☆☆
			☆☆☆☆☆
			☆☆☆☆☆
			☆☆☆☆☆
			☆☆☆☆☆
			☆☆☆☆☆
			☆☆☆☆☆
			☆☆☆☆☆
			☆☆☆☆☆
			☆☆☆☆☆
			☆☆☆☆☆
			☆☆☆☆☆
			☆☆☆☆☆

Reading Log

Title	Author	Date Read	Rating
			☆☆☆☆☆
			☆☆☆☆☆
			☆☆☆☆☆
			☆☆☆☆☆
			☆☆☆☆☆
			☆☆☆☆☆
			☆☆☆☆☆
			☆☆☆☆☆
			☆☆☆☆☆
			☆☆☆☆☆
			☆☆☆☆☆
			☆☆☆☆☆
			☆☆☆☆☆
			☆☆☆☆☆
			☆☆☆☆☆
			☆☆☆☆☆
			☆☆☆☆☆
			☆☆☆☆☆
			☆☆☆☆☆
			☆☆☆☆☆

Title/Author	Podcast	Date Read	My Rating
Gaudy Night Dorothy Sayers	Spring 2019		☆☆☆☆☆
"Araby" James Joyce	Summer 2019		☆☆☆☆☆
"A Defence of Penny Dreadfuls" G. K. Chesteron	Summer 2019		☆☆☆☆☆
"The Garden Party" Katherine Mansfield	Summer 2019		☆☆☆☆☆
"The Adventures of a Shilling" Joseph Addison	Summer 2019		☆☆☆☆☆
"The Necklace" Guy de Maupassant	Summer 2019		☆☆☆☆☆
"Why I Write" George Orwell	Summer 2019		☆☆☆☆☆
"The Celestial Omnibus" E. M. Forster	Summer 2019		☆☆☆☆☆
"The Vulture" Samuel Johnson	Summer 2019		☆☆☆☆☆
An Experiment in Criticism C.S. Lewis	Fall 2019		☆☆☆☆☆
Northanger Abbey Jane Austen	Fall/Winter 2019		☆☆☆☆☆

Title/Author	Podcast	Date Read	My Rating
A Winter's Tale William Shakespeare	Winter 2020		☆☆☆☆☆
"The Importance of Being Earnest" Oscar Wilde	Winter 2020		☆☆☆☆☆
The Great Divorce C. S. Lewis	Spring 2020		☆☆☆☆☆
"Essay on Education" Simon Weil	Spring 2020		☆☆☆☆☆
"The Trojan Women" Euripides	Summer 2020		☆☆☆☆☆
"On Fairy Stories" J. R. R. Tolkien	Summer 2020		☆☆☆☆☆
"Leaf by Niggle" J. R. R. Tolkien	Summer 2020		☆☆☆☆☆
Till We Have Faces C. S. Lewis	Fall 2020		☆☆☆☆☆
Phantastes George MacDonald	Fall/Winter 2020		☆☆☆☆☆
Death on the Nile Agatha Christie	Winter 2021		☆☆☆☆☆
84, Charing Cross Road Helene Hanff	Winter 2021		☆☆☆☆☆

Literary Life Podcast Selections

Title/Author	Podcast	Date Read	My Rating
Silas Marner George Eliot	Winter/Spring 2021		☆ ☆ ☆ ☆ ☆
Death of Ivan Ilyich Leo Tolstoy	Spring 2021		☆ ☆ ☆ ☆ ☆
Don Quixote Miguel de Cervantes	Spring 2021		☆ ☆ ☆ ☆ ☆
Fahrenheit 451 Ray Bradbury	Spring 2021		☆ ☆ ☆ ☆ ☆
Antigone Sophocles	Summer 2021		☆ ☆ ☆ ☆ ☆
How Much Land Does a Man Need? Leo Tolstoy	Summer 2021		☆ ☆ ☆ ☆ ☆
The Machine Stops E. M. Forster	Summer 2021		☆ ☆ ☆ ☆ ☆
Reunion Fred Uhlman	Summer 2021		☆ ☆ ☆ ☆ ☆
The Rocking Horse Winner D. H. Lawrence	Summer 2021		☆ ☆ ☆ ☆ ☆
The Strange Case of Dr. Jekyll and Mr. Hyde Robert Louis Stevenson	Summer 2021		☆ ☆ ☆ ☆ ☆
Mansfield Park Jane Austen	Fall 2021		☆ ☆ ☆ ☆ ☆
"The Masque of the Red Death" Edgar Allan Poe	Halloween Episode 2021		☆ ☆ ☆ ☆ ☆

Literary Life Podcast Selections

Title/Author	Podcast	Date Read	My Rating

Literary Life Podcast Selections

Title/Author	Podcast	Date Read	My Rating

Commonplace Quotes

"I entirely agree that it's no good trying to coerce or argue artists into giving what they haven't got. Either they burst into tears, or go sullen, or—if they are hearty extraverts—they cheerfully turn out fifteen new versions, each worse than the last. Actors too. They're the most kittle cattle of the lot."
—Dorothy Sayers, in a letter to C. S. Lewis (Shared in Podcast Ep. 108)

"Many come to wish their tower a well..."
—W. H. Auden, from "The Quest" (Shared in Podcast Ep. 107)

"She is almost a Jane Austen heroine condemned to a Charlotte Brontë situation. We do not even believe in what Jane Austen tells us of her good looks; whenever we are looking at the action through Fanny's eyes, we feel ourselves sharing the consciousness of a plain woman."
—C. S. Lewis, "A Note on Jane Austen" (Shared in Podcast Ep. 108)

Commonplace Quotes

"Sadly, we do not have a Christian culture today that easily discriminates between a person of spiritual depth and a person of raw talent. Like the wheat and the tares of Jesus' parable, they can be difficult to distinguish. The result is that more than a few people can be fooled into thinking they are being influenced by a spiritual giant when, in fact, they are being manipulated by a dwarf."

—Gordon MacDonald in *Ordering Your Private World* (Shared in Podcast Ep. 107)

Commonplace Quotes

"Would you think I was joking if I said that you can put a clock back, and that if the clock is wrong it is often a very sensible thing to do? But I would rather get away from that whole idea of clocks. We all want to progress. But progress mean getting nearer to the place where you want to be. And if you have taken a wrong turning, then to go forward does not get you any nearer. If you are on the wrong road, progress means doing an about-turn and walking back to the right road; and in that case the man who turns back soonest is the most progressive man.... If you look at the present state of the big mistake. We are on the wrong road. And if that is so, we must go back. Going back is the quickest way on."
—C. S. Lewis in Mere Christianity (Shared in Podcast Ep. 107)

"While affording some secrets of the way of the will to young people, we should perhaps beware of presenting the ideas of self-knowledge, self-reverence, and self-control. All adequate education must be outward bound, and the mind which is concentrated on self-emolument, even though it be the emolument of all the virtues, misses the higher and the simpler secrets of life. Duty and service are the sufficient motives for the arduous training of the will that the child goes through with little consciousness."

—Charlotte Mason in Towards a Philosophy of Education (Shared in Podcast Ep. 108)

"One beautiful starry-skied evening, we two stood next to each other at a window, and I, a young man of about twenty-two who had just eaten well and had good coffee, enthused about the stars and called them the abode of the blessed. But the master grumbled to himself: 'The stars, hum! hum! The stars are only a gleaming leprosy in the sky.'"
—Heinrich Heine in Confessions (Shared in Podcast Ep. 106)

Commonplace Quotes

"It is a mistake, perhaps, to think that, to do one thing well, we must just do and think about that and nothing else all the time. It is our business to know all we can and to spend a part of our lives in increasing our knowledge of Nature and Art, of Literature and Man, of the Past and the Present. That is one way in which we become greater persons, and the more a person is, the better he will do whatever piece of special work falls to his share. Let us have, like Leonardo, a spirit 'invariably royal and magnanimous.'"

—Charlotte Mason, Ourselves (Shared in Podcast Ep. 106)

Commonplace Quotes

"The poet's job is not to tell you what happened, but what happens: not what did take place, but the kind of thing that always takes place."

—Northrop Frye in The Educated Imagination (*Shared in Podcast Ep. 106*)

"I would rather (said he) have the rod to be the general terrour to all, to make them learn, than tell a child, if you do thus, or thus, you will be more esteemed than your brothers or sisters. The rod produces an effect which terminates in itself. A child is afraid of being whipped, and gets his task, and there's an end on't; whereas, by exciting emulation and comparisons of superiority, you lay the foundation of lasting mischief; you make brothers and sisters hate each other."

—Samuel Johnson quoted in Boswell's Life of Samuel Johnson(Shared in Podcast Ep. 105)

"Do not talk about Shakespeare's mistakes: they are probably your own."
—G. M. Young *(Shared in Podcast Ep. 105)*

"The most influential books, and the truest in their influence, are works of fiction. They do not pin the reader to a dogma, which he must afterwards discover to be inexact; they do not teach him a lesson, which he must afterwards unlearn… They disengage us from ourselves, they constrain us to the acquaintance of others; and they show us the web of experience, not as we see it for ourselves, but with a singular change—that monstrous, consuming ego of ours being, for the nonce, struck out."

—Robert Louis Stevenson in an essay, "Books Which Have Influenced Me" (Shared in Podcast Ep. 105)

"I am not conscious of having ever bought a book from a motive of ostentation."
—Edward Gibbon in Memoirs of my Life and Writings (Shared in Podcast Ep. 104)

"There is no language and no knowledge without symbol and metaphor. Two consequences arise from this: one is that we require imagination both to make and to interpret symbols, and the other is that symbols themselves beckon us through language to that which is beyond language. In other words, symbols are energized between the two poles (as Coleridge would say) of immanence and transcendence."

—Malcolm Guite in Faith, Hope and Poetry: Theology and the Poetic Imagination

(Shared in Podcast Ep. 104)

"Incidentally, we do not know of a single healthy and powerful book used to educate people (and that includes the Bible) in which such delicate matters do not actually appear to an even greater extent. Proper usage sees no evil here, but finds, as an attractive saying has it, a document of our hearts. Children can read the stars without fear, while others, so superstition has it, insult angels by doing the same thing."
— Wilhelm Grimm (Shared in Podcast Ep. 104)

Commonplace Quotes

"Rather than being restricted to the simple material they can read on their own, young children need to listen to their teachers read more complex books aloud and engage in discussions about what they've heard—and, depending on their age, write about it. At the same time, teaching disconnected comprehension skills boosts neither comprehension nor reading scores. It's just empty calories. In effect, kids are clamoring for broccoli and spinach while adults insist on a steady diet of donuts."

—Natalie Wexler, The Knowledge Gap (Shared in Podcast Ep. 103)

Commonplace Quotes

"Our proper bliss depends on what we blame."
—Alexander Pope, "Essay on Man" (Shared in Podcast Ep. 103)

"Never trust the artist. Trust the tale.
The proper function of a critic is to save the tale from the artist who created it."
—D. H. Lawrence, Studies in Classic American Literature (Shared in Podcast Ep. 103)

"One's life is more formed, I sometimes think, by books than by human beings: it is out of books one learns about love and pain at second hand. Even if we have the happy chance to fall in love, it is because we have been conditioned by what we have read, and if I had never known love at all, perhaps it was because my father's library had not contained the right books."

—Graham Greene, from Travels with my Aunt (Shared in Podcast Ep. 102)

Commonplace Quotes

"...there is also a sort of wild fairy interest in them, which makes me think them fully better adapted to awaken the imagination and soften the heart of childhood than the good-boy stories which have been in later years composed for them."

——Sir Walter Scott, from German Popular Stories (Shared in Podcast Ep. 102)

Commonplace Quotes

"Information can thrill, but only once."
—Wendell Berry (Shared in Podcast Ep. 102)

Commonplace Quotes

All suffices reckoned rightly:
Spring shall bloom where now the ice is,
Roses make the bramble sightly,
And the quickening sun shine brightly,
And the latter wind blow lightly,
And my garden teem with spices.
—Christina Rossetti, "Amen" (Shared in Podcast Ep. 102)

Commonplace Quotes

"Literature is full of teaching, by precept and example, concerning the management of our physical nature. I shall offer a lesson here and there by way of sample, but no doubt the reader will think of many better teachings; and that is as it should be; the way such teaching should come to us is, here a little and there a little, incidentally, from books which we read for the interest of the story, the beauty of the poem, or the grace of the writing."
—Charlotte Mason in Ourselves (Shared in Podcast Ep. 101)

"If you've got something you want to say,
just think first as to whether it's really worthwhile, and you're sure to find that it isn't."
Hugh Walpole, "The Enemy in Ambush" (Shared in Podcast Ep. 100)

"I acquired a hunger for fairy tales in the dark days of blackout and blitz in the Second World War. I read early and voraciously and indiscriminately—Andrew Lang's colored Fairy Book, Hans Andersen, King Arthur, Robin Hood, and my very favorite book, Asgard and the Gods, a German scholarly text, with engravings, about Norse mythology, which my mother had used as a crib in her studies of Ancient Norse…

"...I never really like stories about children doing what children do—quarreling and cooking and camping. I like magic, the unreal, the more than real. I learned from the Asgard book that even the gods can be defeated by evil. I knew nothing about the Wagnerian Nordic pageantry of the Third Reich. Nor did I have any inkling that the British occupying forces in Germany after the war were going to ban the Grimms because they fed a supposedly bloodthirsty German imagination. Indeed, I retreated into them from wartime anxieties."

—A. S. Byatt in his Introduction to The Grimm Reader (Shared in Podcast Ep. 101)

"Every fairy tale worth recording at all is the remnant of tradition possessing true historical value; historical, at least, insofar as it has arisen out of the mind of a people under special circumstance, and risen not without meaning, nor removed altogether from their sphere of religious faith."

—John Ruskin in his Introduction to Grimms' German Popular Stories (Shared in Podcast Ep. 101)

Commonplace Quotes

"The vicar's wife would not be quite that endless whimper of self-pity which she now is, if she did not in a sense "love" the family. The continued disappointment of her continued and ruthless demand for sympathy, for affection, for appreciation has helped to make her what she is. The greed to be loved is a fearful thing. Some of those who say, and almost with pride, that they live only for love, come at last to live in incessant resentment."

C. S. Lewis in his essay "The Sermon and the Lunch" (Shared in Podcast Ep. 100)

"*Lastly, from the properties (the castle on the mountain, the cottage in the wood, the helpful beasts, the guardian dragons, the cave, the fountain, the trysting lane, etc.), he will acquire the basic symbols to which he can add railway trains, baths, wrist-watches and what-have-you from his own experience, and so build up a web of associations…*

Commonplace Quotes

...which are the only means by which his inner and outer life, his past and his present, can be related to, and mentally enrich, each other. Half our troubles, both individual neuroses and collective manias like nationalism, seem to me to be caused largely by our poverty of symbols, so that not only do we fail to relate one experience to another but also we have to entrust our whole emotional life to the few symbols we do have."

W.H. Auden, "In Praise of the Brothers Grimm,"
The New York Times Book Review, 12 November 1944 (Shared in Podcast Ep. 100)

Commonplace Quotes

"Imagination, in its earthbound quest,
Seeks in the infinite its finite rest."
—Walter de la Mare (from "Books") (Shared in Podcast Ep. 99)

*"All true poetry can be interpreted in manifold different ways,
for it has arisen from life and it returns back to life. It hits us like sunshine
no matter where we are standing. For that reason a moral precept or a relevant object lesson can be readily
derived from these tales; it was never their purpose to instruct, nor were they made up for that reason, but a
moral grows out of them, just as good fruit develops from healthy blossoms without help from man."*
—Wilhelm Grimm (Shared in Podcast Ep. 97)

Commonplace Quotes

"You don't know what ideas my mind-spirit needs right now; I don't know what your mind-spirit needs; and we don't know the mind-spirit needs of each child in a classroom. Vital ideas are not sold pre-measured in a bottle."
—Anne White, author of Ideas Freely Sown (Shared in Podcast Ep. 96)

"She had a terror of solitary evenings, all the terror of one who did not care for books, who was soaked in
superstition and loved lights and noise."

—Hugh Walpole, from the short story "Fanny Close" (Shared in Podcast Ep. 96)

"When we are self-conscious, we cannot be wholly aware; we must throw ourselves out first. This throwing ourselves away is the act of creativity. So, when we wholly concentrate, like a child in play, or an artist at work, then we share in the act of creating. We not only escape time, we also escape our self-conscious selves...

…The Greeks had a word for ultimate self-consciousness which I find illuminating: hubris: pride: pride in the sense of putting oneself in the center of the universe. The strange and terrible thing is that this kind of total self-consciousness invariably ends in self-annihilation. The great tragedians have always understood this, from Sophocles to Shakespeare."

—Madeleine L'Engle, A Circle of Quiet (Shared in Podcast Ep. 96)

"That best portion of a good man's life,
  His little, nameless, unremembered acts
  Of kindness and of love…"
—William Wordsworth, "Lines Composed a Few Miles above Tintern Abbey, On Revisiting the Banks of the
  Wye during a Tour, July 13, 1798" (Shared in Podcast Ep. 95)

"That men have been burnt alive willingly is a fact of no little interest to anyone who has ever put his hand in the flame of a candle."
—G. K. Chesterton (Shared in Podcast Ep. 95)

Commonplace Quotes

"The poem is a great palace, but the door into it is so low that you must stoop to go in. No prig can be a Spenserian. It is, of course, much more than a fairy tale, but unless we can enjoy it as a fairy tale first of all, we shall not really care for it."
—C. S. Lewis, Studies in Medieval and Renaissance Literature (*Shared in Podcast Ep. 95*)

Commonplace Quotes

"I chose books that I wanted to read for my own education and brought the children along with me. This made homeschooling and morning time a feast for my soul as well as theirs."
—Jami Marstall (Shared in Podcast Ep. 95)

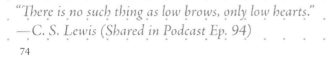
"There is no such thing as low brows, only low hearts."
—C. S. Lewis (Shared in Podcast Ep. 94)

Commonplace Quotes

"More unsolicited advice: if you really want a well-read, well-educated child, you will stop dropping books or subjects just because he doesn't think he likes them. Education is the development of taste, not the reinforcement of a child's lack of it."

—Brandy Vencel (Shared in Podcast Ep. 94)

"People ask me to predict the future when all I want to do is prevent it."
—Ray Bradbury, Beyond 1984: The People Machines (1979) (Shared in Podcast Ep. 94)

"Long and delicate maneuverings had bred in him a habit of deceit, and his success had convinced him that in politics, dishonesty was but a venial offense."
—J. D. Mackie (Shared in Podcast Ep. 93)

Commonplace Quotes

"I would not have you think I was doing nothing then." He might, perhaps, have studied more assiduously; but it may be doubted whether such a mind as his was not more enriched by roaming at large in the fields of literature than if it had been confined to any single spot. The analogy between body and mind is very general, and the parallel will hold as to their food, as well as any other particular…

...The flesh of animals who feed excursively, is allowed to have a higher flavour than that of those who are cooped up. May there not be the same difference between men who read as their taste prompts and men who are confined in cells and colleges to stated tasks?

—Samuel Johnson quoted in Boswell's Life of Samuel Johnson (Shared in Podcast Ep. 93)

Interviewer: "How does the story of Fahrenheit 451 stand up in 1994?"

Ray Bradbury: "It works even better because we have political correctness now. Political correctness is the real enemy these days…It's thought control and freedom of speech control."

—Ray Bradbury (Shared in Podcast Ep. 93)

"If someone tells you what a story is about, they are probably right. If they tell you that that is all the story is about, they are very definitely wrong."

—Neil Gaiman (Shared in Podcast Ep. 92)

Commonplace Quotes

"It will be a bad day for England when we have done with Shakespeare; for that will imply, along with the loss of him, that we are no longer capable of understanding him."
—George MacDonald in A Dish of Orts (Shared in Podcast Ep. 92)

"Libraries raised me. I don't believe in colleges and universities. I believe in libraries because most students don't have any money. When I graduated from high school it was during the Depression, and we had no money. I couldn't go to college, so I went to the library three days a week for ten years."
—Ray Bradbury (Shared in Podcast Ep. 92)

"The only inconvenience is that none of these projects are yet brought to perfection, and in the meantime the whole country lies miserably waste, the houses in ruins and the people without food or clothes. By all which, instead of being discouraged, they are fifty times more violently bent upon prosecuting their schemes, driven equally on by hope and despair."

—Jonathon Swift, Gulliver's Travels (Shared in Podcast Ep. 91)

"The humanities do not always make a man humane—that is, liberal, tolerant, gentle, and candid as regards the opinions and status of other men. The fault does not lie in any one of these or in any other of the disciplinary subjects, but in our indolent habit of using each of these as a sort of mechanical contrivance for turning up the soil and sowing the seed."

—Charlotte Mason, School Education (Shared in Podcast Ep. 91)

Commonplace Quotes

"I should be cautious of censuring anything that has been applauded by so many suffrages."
—Samuel Johnson quoted in Boswell's Life of Samuel Johnson (Shared in Podcast Ep. 91)

"Arrogance is a weed that ever grows in a dunghill."
—Owen Feltham in "Resolves" (Shared in Podcast Ep. 90)

"To enhance the wonder, see
How arch his notices, how nice his sense
Of the ridiculous; …he can read
The inside of the earth, and spell the stars;
He knows the policies of foreign lands;
Can string you names of districts, cities, towns,
The whole world over, tight as beads of dew
Upon a gossamer thread; he sifts, he weighs;
All things are put to question; he must live
Knowing that he grows wiser every day,
Or else not live at all, and seeing too
Each little drop of wisdom as it falls
Into the dimpling cistern of his heart:
For this unnatural growth the trainer blame,
Pity the tree…

"Meanwhile old grandame earth is grieved to find
The playthings, which her love designed for him,
Unthought of: in their woodland beds the flowers
Weep, and the river sides are all forlorn.
Oh! give us once again the wishing-cap
Of Fortunatus, and the invisible coat
Of Jack the Giant-killer, Robin Hood,
And Sabra in the forest with St George!
The child, whose love is here, at least, doth reap
One precious gain, that he forgets himself."
—William Wordsworth, from "Prelude" (Shared in Podcast Ep. 90)

"[Fairy stories] never seek to criticize or moralize, to protest or plead or persuade; and if they have an emotional impact on the reader, as the greatest of them to, that is not intrinsic to the stories. They would indeed only weaken that impact in direct proportion as soon as they set out to achieve it. They move by not seeking to move; almost, it seems, by seeking not to move. The fairy-story that succeeds is in fact not a work of fiction at all; . . . It is a transcription of a view of life into terms of highly simplified symbols; and when it succeeds in its literary purpose, it leaves us with a deep indefinable feeling of truth."
—C. M. Woodhouse, on *Animal Farm*, The Times Literary Supplement, 1954 (*Shared in Podcast Ep. 90*)

"Whenever we are called to teach, our proclamation of goodness should be so wrapped in beauty as to console. This should apply to our daily actions as well, and it is an art."

Timothy Patitsas, author of The Ethics of Beauty (Shared in Podcast Ep. 89)

Commonplace Quotes

"Even if I knew that tomorrow the world would go to pieces, I would still plant my apple tree."
Attributed to Martin Luther (Shared in Podcast Ep. 89)

Commonplace Quotes

"Books serve to show a man that those original thoughts of his aren't very new at all."
—attributed to Abraham Lincoln (Shared in Podcast Ep. 88)

Commonplace Quotes

"I take it to be part and parcel of the same great process of Internalisation which has turned genius from an attendant daemon into a quality of the mind. Always, century by century, item after item is transferred from the object's side of the account to the subject's. And now, in some extreme forms of Behaviourism, the subject himself is discounted as merely subjective; we only think that we think. Having eaten up everything else, he eats himself up too. And where we 'go from that' is a dark question."
C. S. Lewis, The Discarded Image (Shared in Podcast Ep. 88)

Commonplace Quotes

"Suppose you were an idiot. And suppose you were a member of Congress. But I repeat myself."
Mark Twain (Shared in Podcast Ep. 88)

"I don't like the word 'allegorical.' I don't like the word 'symbolic.' The word I really like is 'mythic,' and people always think that means 'full of lies' when what it really means is full of a truth that cannot be told in any other way but a story."

William Golding, author of Lord of the Flies, in a BBC interview (Shared in Podcast Ep. 88)

"I have called this work 'meadow' on account of the delight, the fragrance and the benefit which it will afford those who come across it, for the virtuous life and the habitual piety do not merely consist of studying divinity, not only of thinking on an elevated plane about things as they are here and now..they must also include the description and writing of the way of life of others. So I have striven to complete this composition to inform your love, oh child, and as I have put together a copious and accurate collection, so I have emulated the most wise bee, gathering up the spiritually beneficial deeds of the fathers."

John Moschos, The Spiritual Meadow (Shared in Podcast Ep. 87)

Commonplace Quotes

"The fact that various persons have written angrily to say that the Judas I have depicted seems to them to be a person of the utmost nobility, actuated by extremely worthy motives, confirms my impression that this particular agent of hell is at present doing his master's work with singular thoroughness and success. His exploits go unrecognized – which is just what the devil likes best."
Dorothy Sayers, Introduction to The Man Born to Be King (Shared in Podcast Ep. 87)

Commonplace Quotes

"People enter politics or the Civil Service out of a desire to exert power and influence events; this, I maintain, is an illness. It is only when one realizes that great administrators and leaders of men have all been at any rate slightly mad that one has a true understanding of history."

Auberon Waugh (Shared in Podcast Ep. 87)

"In essence, Tolkien was trying to recover the vision of Eden, the childhood of the race, when beauty was still connected with truth. Through story—the right kind of story, including traditional legends and fairy-tales—the ability to see all things with a pure heart and in the light of heaven could be evoked. He wanted to prove that poetic knowledge, George MacDonald's 'wise imagination,' could be awoken even in a world apparently closed to its very possibility."
Stratford Caldecott (Shared in Podcast Ep. 87)

"We are all willing enough to praise freedom when she is safely tucked away in the past and cannot be a nuisance. In the present, amidst dangers whose outcome we cannot foresee, we get nervous about her, and admit censorship."

—E. M. Forster (Shared in Podcast Ep. 86)

"Our Ford himself did a great deal to shift the emphasis from truth and beauty to comfort and happiness. Mass production demanded the shift. Universal happiness keep the wheels steadily turning; truth and beauty can't."
Aldous Huxley, Brave New World (Shared in Podcast Ep. 86)

Commonplace Quotes

The worst evil in the world is brought about not by the open and self-confessed vices but by the deadly corruption of the proud virtues.

Dorothy Sayers, The Man Born to Be King (Shared in Podcast Ep. 86)

"Idleness is a disease which must be combated; but I would not advise a rigid adherence to a particular plan of study. I myself have never persisted in any plan for two days together. A man ought to read just as inclination leads him; for what he reads as a task will do him little good. A young man should read five hours in a day, and so may acquire a great deal of knowledge."

Samuel Johnson quoted in Boswell's Life of Samuel Johnson (Shared in Podcast Ep. 85)

"Philosophy, like medicine, has a great number of drugs, and precious few genuine remedies."
Nicolas de Chamfort, The Cynic's Breviary; Maxims and Anecdotes *(Shared in Podcast Ep. 85)*

"The feudal ownership of land did bring dignity, whereas the modern ownership of moveables is reducing us again to a nomadic horde. We are reverting to the civilization of luggage, and historians of the future will note how the middle classes accreted possessions without taking root in the earth, and may find in this the secret of their imaginative poverty."

E. M. Forster, Howards End (Shared in Podcast Ep. 85)

"Perhaps the first thing that he can learn from the artist is that the only way of 'mastering' one's material is to abandon the whole conception of mastery and to co-operate with it in love: whosoever will be a lord of life, let him be its servant."

Dorothy Sayers, The Mind of the Maker: The Expression of Faith through Creativity and Art (Shared in Podcast Ep. 84)

"You said that we owe literature almost everything we are and what we have been. If books disappear, history will disappear, and human beings will also disappear. I am sure you are right. Books are not only the arbitrary sum of our dreams, and our memory. They also give us the model of transcendence. Some people think of reading only as a kind of escape: an escape from the 'real' everyday world to an imaginary world, the world of books. Books are much more. They are way of being more fully human."

Susan Sontag, "Love Letter to Borges, Written 10 Years After His Death" (Shared in Podcast Ep. 84)

"A poem can be like two hands that lift you up and put you down in a new place. You look back with astonishment and find that because you have read a few lines on a printed page or listened for a couple of minutes to a voice speaking, you have arrived at somewhere quite different".
Elizabeth Goudge, Towers in the Mist (Shared in Podcast Ep. 83)

"Wheresoe'er I turn my view,
All is strange, yet nothing new;
Endless labour all along,
Endless labour to be wrong..."
Samuel Johnson quoted in Boswell's Life of Samuel Johnson (Shared in Podcast Ep. 83)

"These fellow mortals, every one, must be accepted as they are. You can neither straighten their noses, nor brighten their wits, nor rectify their dispositions; and it is these people amongst whom your life is passed, that it is needful you should tolerate, pity and love."
George Eliot, Adam Bede (Shared in Podcast Ep. 83)

Commonplace Quotes

"Sorrow is knowledge: they who know the most
Must mourn the deepest o'er the fatal truth,
The Tree of Knowledge is not that of Life."
Lord Byron, from "Manfred" (Shared in Podcast Ep. 82)

"God is a mystery and not a fellow conspirator."
J. B. Priestley (Shared in Podcast Ep. 82)

Commonplace Quotes

"There seems good reason to believe that the limit to human intelligence arises largely from the limit to human interests."
Charlotte Mason, School Education (Shared in Podcast Ep. 82)

"He was fortified by illimitable reading, by a present sense of a thousand possibilities that had been brought to pass, of a thousand things so wisely said that wise action was a necessary outcome."
Charlotte Mason, Towards A Philosophy of Education (Shared in Podcast Ep. 82)

"The thing is to keep your eye upon words and wait to feel their force and beauty, and when words are so fit that no other words can be put in their places, so few that none can be left out without spoiling the sense, and so fresh and musical that they delight you, then you may be sure that you are reading literature, whether in prose or poetry."
Charlotte Mason, Ourselves (Shared in Podcast Ep. 82)

"Men are apt to prefer a prosperous error before an afflicted truth."
Jeremy Taylor, The Rules and Exercises of Holy Living (Shared in Podcast Ep. 81)

"Secondhand booksellers are the most friendly and most eccentric of all the characters I have known. If I had not been a writer, theirs would have been the profession I would most happily have chosen."
Graham Greene in his Introduction to David Low's memoir (Shared in Podcast Ep. 81)

Book Reviews

My Review

Title:

Author:

Date Read:

Rating: ☆ ☆ ☆ ☆ ☆

My Review

Title:

Author:

Date Read:

Rating: ☆ ☆ ☆ ☆ ☆

My Review

Title:

Author:

Date Read:

Rating: ☆ ☆ ☆ ☆ ☆

My Review

Title:

Author:

Date Read:

Rating: ☆ ☆ ☆ ☆ ☆

My Review

Title:

Author:

Date Read:

Rating: ☆ ☆ ☆ ☆ ☆

My Review

Title:

Author:

Date Read:

Rating: ☆ ☆ ☆ ☆ ☆

My Review

Title:

Author:

Date Read:

Rating: ☆ ☆ ☆ ☆ ☆

☆ ★

My Review

Title:

Author:

Date Read:

Rating: ☆ ☆ ☆ ☆ ☆

My Review

Title:

Author:

Date Read:

Rating: ☆ ☆ ☆ ☆ ☆

My Review

Title:

Author:

Date Read:

Rating: ☆ ☆ ☆ ☆ ☆

My Review

Title:

Author:

Date Read:

Rating: ☆ ☆ ☆ ☆ ☆

My Review

Title:

Author:

Date Read:

Rating: ☆☆☆☆☆

My Review

Title:

Author:

Date Read:

Rating: ☆ ☆ ☆ ☆ ☆

My Review

Title:

Author:

Date Read:

Rating: ☆ ☆ ☆ ☆ ☆

My Review

Title:

Author:

Date Read:

Rating: ☆ ☆ ☆ ☆ ☆

My Review

Title:

Author:

Date Read:

Rating: ☆ ☆ ☆ ☆ ☆

My Review

Title:

Author:

Date Read:

Rating: ☆ ☆ ☆ ☆ ☆

Title:

Author:

Date Read:

Rating: ☆ ☆ ☆ ☆ ☆

My Review

Title:

Author:

Date Read:

Rating: ☆ ☆ ☆ ☆ ☆

My Review

Title:

Author:

Date Read:

Rating: ☆ ☆ ☆ ☆ ☆

Title:

Author:

Date Read:

Rating: ☆ ☆ ☆ ☆ ☆

Stories will save the world.

Angelina Stanford

Angelina Stanford has an Honors Baccalaureate Degree and a Master's Degree in English Literature from the University of Louisiana, graduating Phi Kappa Phi. For over twenty-five years, she has shared her passion and enthusiasm for literature with students in a variety of settings and is a popular conference speaker and podcast guest. In 2020, with her husband, Thomas Banks, she founded the House of Humane Letters, providing classes, webinars, conferences and other resources for a more humane education. Angelina maintains a high commitment to teaching teachers and students the skill and art of reading well—and in recapturing the tradition of literary scholarship needed to fully engage with the Great Books. She is a great believer that Stories Will Save the World!

Cindy Rollins

Cindy Rollins homeschooled her nine children for over thirty years. She is a co-host with Angelina Stanford and Thomas Banks of the popular Literary Life Podcast and curates the "Over the Back Fence Newsletter" at CindyRollins.net. She is the author of *Morning Time: A Liturgy of Love*; *Mere Motherhood: Morning Time, Nursery Rhymes, and My Journey Toward Sanctification*; the *Mere Motherhood Newsletters*; and *Hallelujah: Cultivating Advent Traditions with Handel's Messiah*.

Cindy runs an active Patreon group where the participants read Charlotte Mason's volumes and discuss questions pertaining to motherhood and life. Her heart's desire is to encourage moms using Charlotte Mason's timeless principles. She lives in Chattanooga, Tennessee, with her husband, Tim, and dog, Max. She also travels around the country visiting her 13 grandchildren, watching her youngest son play baseball, and occasionally speaking at events.

Thomas Banks

Thomas Banks has taught great books with an emphasis on Greek and Roman literature, Latin grammar and ancient history for more than ten years both as a private tutor and as a junior high and high school teacher in his native Idaho and Montana. He holds a dual bachelor's degree in English Literature and Classical Studies from the University of Idaho, from which he graduated in 2008. In the summer of 2019, he moved to North Carolina to marry the illustrious Ms. Angelina Stanford, who said yes for some reason.

Poetry is a particular love of his, and he has published original verse and translations in First Things, the St. Austin Review and various other periodicals. His personal list of favorite writers never really stops growing, but will always include Homer, Euripides, Virgil, Ovid, St. Augustine, Shakespeare, Samuel Johnson, Byron, Keats, Walter Scott and Thomas Hardy. Of these and so many others one cannot have enough.

Thomas Banks currently resides in North Carolina, where he teaches Latin, literature and history online with his wife Angelina Stanford at The House of Humane Letters. His poetry, translations and other writings have appeared in First Things, The Imaginative Conservative, The New English Review, and various other publications.

Other Blue Sky Daisies Titles

By Cindy Rollins
Morning Time: A Liturgy of Love by Cindy Rollins
Hallelujah: Cultivating Advent Traditions with Handel's Messiah by Cindy Rollins

Geography Books
Elementary Geography by Charlotte Mason
Home Geography for Primary Grades with Written and Oral Exercises by C. C. Long

Language Arts and Grammar Books
The Mother Tongue: Adapted for Modern Students by George Lyman Kittredge. In this series: Workbook 1 and 2; Answer Key 1 and 2
Exercises in Dictation by F. Peel
Grammar Land: Grammar in Fun for the Children of Schoolroom Shire (Annotated) By M. L. Nesbitt. Annotated by Amy M. Edwards and Christina J. Mugglin

The CopyWorkBook Series
The CopyWorkBook: George Washington's Rules of Civility & Decent Behavior in Company and Conversation by Amy M. Edwards and Christina J. Mugglin
The CopyWorkBook: Comedies of William Shakespeare by Amy M. Edwards and Christina J. Mugglin

Other Titles
The Birds' Christmas Carol by Kate Douglas Wiggin
The Innkeeper's Daughter by Michelle Lallement
Kipling's Rikki-Tikki-Tavi: A Children's Play by Amy M. Edwards

*These titles are popular with those inspired by Charlotte Mason and her educational philosophy.

Made in the USA
Las Vegas, NV
06 December 2022

61307634R00079